SPEAKING OF MATH

Fluency Poems For Partners: Addition

Written by Janet Lynne (Hagemeyer) Tassell, Ph.D. and Brad Lee Tassell

Illustrated by Nathan Hendricksen

www.speakingofmath.org

This book is dedicated to:

Darby – Our clever daughter, lover of books, gave us the inspiration for this book when she was a 4-year-old!

Ben & Gracie Prather – Yes, we were thinking of you too as we wrote these books! We knew you would like the strong vocabulary and brilliant illustrations!

WKU ELED 405 Math Methods Students, Fall 2008-Spring 2012 – Thank you for letting us try out our ideas with you!

North Spencer County School Corporation elementary teachers.

Thanks to the editors:

Emily Harrod, DeeAnn Hagemeyer, Ellen Micheletti, Sara Prather

Design and pre-press:

Patty Walsh, patty@pattywalsh.com

For further information:

www.speakingofmath.org

Published by And Books, South Bend, Indiana

ISBN-13: 978-089708-237-2
ISBN-10: 0-89708-237-0
Library of Congress Control Number: 2012940554

10 9 8 7 6 5 4 3 2 1

Printed in the U.S.A.
First printing, May, 2012

Fluency In Mathematics

With so many children (and adults) in the United States saying that they can't do math, or they don't like math, it is critical that students develop a love for mathematics as well as competency and confidence in their mathematical abilities. As they read the stories in Speaking of Math, students learn that not only can math be lots of fun, but also that math is a social activity that they can master and share with peers, families, and many others.

Using models such as ten frames to illustrate what they are reading is a great way for children to make sense of the mathematics while they are having fun with the stories. Modeling what is happening in the stories using chips, pennies or other small markers gives them a visual image of the amounts mentioned and lets them see numbers as concrete amounts and not just numerals on a page.

The suggestion to have students write their own stories is a great one. Mathematics should be viewed as a creative activity, and encouraging children to write their own mathematical stories not only exercises their creativity, but also deepens their mathematical understanding and computational fluency.

And we have all heard the phrase "laughter is the best medicine". There is actually a field of study of the neurological effects of laughter called gelotology. Apparently research has shown that laughter helps the brain regulate dopamine, which affects not only mood, but also attention, motivation and learning. When children are engaged, challenged and having fun, memory is enhanced and learning improved. Speaking of Math seems like a great way to get students hooked on becoming fluent with addition facts in a fun and engaging way.

Linda Sheffield, Ph. D.
Regents Professor Emerita, Mathematics Education

Fluency in Reading

As a former Title I Literacy Consultant and current principal of a National Blue Ribbon school, I am delighted to offer praise to this unique genre of books that provides a wonderful experience for the reader. This kind of literature provides the easiest and most enjoyable way for parents to help and motivate their children to read confidently! And now, we not only have poetry that improves fluency and reading development, but also focuses on an important content area - mathematics! This innovative approach to building fluency, confidence and reading ability is a must have in any strong reading program.

Julie Kemp

ABOUT THIS BOOK

Speaking of Math was designed out of a love for reading and watching our daughter grow up wanting to "play" with books more than any other toy. Realizing this, we readily began seeking out different formats to engage her growth in different aspects of reading skills. We wanted her to be a fluent reader and enjoy rich vocabulary. We found that she loved the format of partner reading in two voices. We wanted her to develop the same love for mathematics. However, we did not find a book that addressed mathematics fluency in any way. Hence, our stories are born!

How to Use this Book

The Common Core Standards addressed in this book focus on Number and Operations in Base Ten, the cornerstone of K-6 mathematics, as we are working predominantly on the foundation of adding numbers 0-11. The National Math Panel Report (2008) requests that curriculum should simultaneously develop conceptual understanding, computational fluency, and problem-solving skills. Our hope with these stories is to provide an enhancement to the computational fluency angle of the curriculum. We also believe that this sets a strong foundation for students practicing the Standards for Mathematical Practice, especially number six, "Attend to Precision." In this, students work on communicating "precisely to others" and discussing their reasoning with others. The stories are designed around this notion.

We have a story for each number and a "bonus" story for "Minus 9". This book may be used in several ways ~ consider centers! This is a great way to incorporate differentiation into the setting and address learning needs by interest, readiness, or learning style.

Partner Reading:

Students may be paired homogeneously or heterogeneously by reading and/or by mathematics fluency levels to work on skills as they read the book together. They would be seated throughout the room, shoulder to shoulder, smiling and reading aloud. The person on the left reads the red; the person on the right reads the blue. Together, the two read the purple. This can also be used in a group format AND at home for family reading!

Manipulatives:

Students may, of course, be using manipulatives as they are working on the stories! Perhaps for the first reading, the pair reads through for reading fluency. The second reading may be for pausing at each math problem to model visually what is taking place in the story. Ten frames are great for this.

Technology:

Student use of technology would be a wonderful way to show their understanding of what they are learning and applying from the reading. For example, as a companion to the story, students can write their own stories and illustrate this through StoryBird. Students can also do presentations of their understanding of their different "facts" by creating a Glogster or a Prezi with multimedia facets. This may take much support from the teacher and may need to be done as a class or group project depending on the age of the students. Of course, students writing and illustrating their own number stories using old-fashioned paper and pencil can also create delightful stories while deepening understanding of addition facts.

CONTENTS

ZERO KNOWS YOUR NAME!

Plus 0

Zero is very smart.

A number that's smart?

Smart for a start!

But zero is nothing – zero is zip!

But zero is smart - as smart as a whip!

Are you making fun? Is this a game?

I'm not making fun, and it's not a game.
Zero is so smart, it remembers every
number's name.

**Add all the numbers by zero,
one to nine.**

Will it remember
their names?

It will do just fine.

Zero plus one
is a good place
to begin.

I'm ready
to go.
I'll jump
right in!

Zero plus
one...

Easily done!

It's 1!
Zero plus one equals one. The answer is fun!

Zero plus two...

It's easy, it's true.

It's 2!
Zero plus two, equals two.
What else can we do?

Zero plus three...

It's easy to see.

It's 3!
Zero plus three, equals three.
What else could it be?

Zero plus four...

I know the score!

It's 4!
Zero plus four equals four.
More, more, more!

I get it now. I think I know how!

Great news!

Add to zero any number you choose!

Repeat the number, and we can't lose!

Zero plus five equals five!
Zero plus six equals six!

Zero plus seven, equals seven.
Zero plus eight, equals eight.

Zero plus nine is nine every time!

Zero knows.

And now so do I! But what about zero plus zero?
Can we play the same game?

Yes, you can.

Zero says its own name. Zero plus zero is... zero!

ANTS IN OUR TUMMY
Plus 1

Adding by one. It's easy! It's fun!

And like eating yummy ants, put them on your tongue.
Gulp, and you are done.

Some will not eat ants.
They say it's crazy, we're gross!

But my mouth starts to water.
I love them with honey on toast.

Pick up one ant. Put it on your tongue.

$$1 + 0 = 1$$

One ant on your tongue. Don't swallow yet.

Add one more ant. How many do you get?

$$1 + 1 = 2$$

Now you've got two.
Add one more ant, and you'll see.

Crawling on your tongue is ant number three.

$$1 + 2 = 3$$

A fourth off the ground, and up to my mouth.

Soon we will swallow, and the bugs will go south.

$$1 + 3 = 4$$

More ants, more ants, what a great game!

When it comes to ones,
adding and eating are the same.

One more ant, and we go from four to five.

Thirty little legs on our tongues,

very much alive.

$$1 + 4 = 5$$

They are crawling on my teeth.
They are dancing across my gums.

I can't think of a better way to work on our sums.

One more ant down the hatch,
a creepy, crawly, tasty catch.

$1 + 5 = 6$

How many ants can we fit in this mix?

One more ant and that makes seven. One more after that and it's eight.

If one tastes really good, go back and eat his mate.

$1 + 6 = 7$

$1 + 7 = 8$

Close your mouth before it's too late!

Just two more and then it's right down my throat.

My tummy is so happy, I might just gloat.

$1 + 8 = 9$, just fine.

$1 + 9 = 10$, and then?

Close your mouth, and down they go.

They'll wiggle in my tummy,
it's all part of the show.

My stomach is so happy, without any cares.
You know we love to eat ants,
because of course, we are bears.

TWIN TONGUES

Plus 2

Without fingers or toes, snakes still must learn to count.
So adding is easy when we stick our tongues out.

The snakes in our class learned adding by two
by counting our tongues and giggling too.

Mrs. Boa our teacher explained since
our rattlers are twins,

Adding our tongues to theirs
would help the learning begin.

Teacher said: Adding by two is like adding by one.
Just put one more on, and the answer is done.

Our rattler friends look exactly alike.

So, we added both their tongues together,
just like one, only twice.

We started with no tongues.

Then two hit the air.

$$0 + 2 = 2$$

Our rattler friends are a super fun pair.

Tongues back in.

Let's start again.

Sidewinder's tongue out...

then add the twins.

$$1 + 2 = 3$$

A nest full of grins!

Now Sidewinder and Coral,
tongues past your lips.

Add the twins now,
like slithery strips.

$$2 + 2 = 4$$

Sidewinder, Coral, and Grass...

Plus our two rattlers, and
the test they will pass.

$$3 + 2 = 5$$

Sidewinder, Coral, Grass, and King...

Twin Rattler tongues out,
a natural snake thing.

$$4 + 2 = 6$$

Sidewinder, Coral, Grass, King, and Corn...

Add our twin tongues,
and a learning game's born.

$$5 + 2 = 7$$

Sidewinder, Coral, Grass, King,
Corn, and Brown...

Two same snake tongues,
slink out and right down.

$$6 + 2 = 8$$

Sidewinder, Coral, Grass, King,
Corn, Brown, and Rat...

Plus our two rattlers,
We'll add up all that.

$$7 + 2 = 9$$

Sidewinder, Coral, Grass, King,
Corn, Brown, Rat, and Ground...

Two more identical tongues
come out with a slithery sound.

$$8 + 2 = 10$$

Sidewinder, Coral, Grass, King,
Corn, Brown, Rat, Ground, and Adder.

Rattler tongues out,
and the math is what matters.

$$9 + 2 = 11$$

Now read this with friends,
and pretend you're all snakes,

And you'll all add by two,
and make no mistakes.

THREE BEANS IN A TROLL'S NOSE
Plus 3

There's a troll named Mort,
who is not the smartest sort.

A troll is not known for his brain.

It was something Mort chose,
to put three beans up his nose...

Which would surely cause real people pain.

Three beans in a nostril of a troll is not smart.
We thought that was all, but it was only a start.

Three beans in one nostril,

Zero beans in the other,

Equals three beans in snot totally covered.

$$3 + 0 = 3$$

Mort laughed a troll laugh,
a laugh he could not hide...

Then stuffed one more bean up
the other hole's side.

Three beans in one place...

And one in the other.

Equals four beans.
Don't tell your mother.

$$3 + 1 = 4$$

But one bean was too small,
and it fell right out.

So Mort shoved in two,
right up his snout.

Three beans in his left side...

Two beans in his right.

Equals five beans stuffed out of sight.

$$3 + 2 = 5$$

But two would not hold,
and they fell to the floor.

Three pushed in the troll.
Are his sinuses sore?

Three beans up here,

Three beans up there,

Equals six beans. All troll boogers beware!

$$3 + 3 = 6$$

All six beans stayed.
The troll liked his new game.

He blew three from one nostril,
pushed up four more without shame.

Four beans in one nostril...

Three beans up the other one, too.

Equals seven beans. Stuck just like glue!

$$3 + 4 = 7$$

Then he blew out the four...

and then up went five.

Equals eight beans, just like a bean hive.

$$3 + 5 = 8$$

Out with the five...

And six take their place,

Equals nine beans, taking up troll nosy space.

$$3 + 6 = 9$$

Six snotty beans shot toward the wall.

Replaced by seven, Mort laughs through it all.

Equals ten beans, in a gooey old ball.

$$3 + 7 = 10$$

Goodbye to seven.

Hello to eight.

Equals eleven beans. Don't ever put these on my plate!

$$3 + 8 = 11$$

All eight beans out.

Nine beans... up they go.

Equals twelve beans. I think Mort's head might just blow.

$$3 + 9 = 12$$

KABOOM!

I have troll snot and beans, from my head to my toes!

We learned that you never put anything in your nose.

T-REX TEETH

Plus 4

While digging in my yard
for worms and for slugs,

We found four T-Rex teeth
underneath all the bugs.

Four teeth plus zero teeth equals four teeth.

The fossils came out
without too many tugs.

I think if we dig,
and sift some more dirt...

We'll uncover more teeth
from under the earth.

Here is a tooth,
underneath an old root.

Was T-Rex hit in the mouth
by someone's old boot?

Four teeth plus one tooth equals five teeth.

Let's look for more loot.

Two teeth in the mud,
under red mushy clay...

Did our dino bite a pot?
Have his teeth fallen away?

Four teeth plus two teeth equals six teeth.

It was hard to find a dentist
in the dinosaur's day.

Under a mole,
three teeth soon appear...

From fangs in the ground,
moles have nothing to fear.

Four teeth plus three teeth equals seven teeth.

There must be more near.

I found four more teeth.
stuck in a bone!

His lunch got away,
and he had to limp home.

Four teeth plus four teeth equals eight teeth.

Eight missing teeth
he won't have when full grown.

Five teeth I found
mixed with pebbles and soil.

All that was left
when T-Rex turned to oil.

Four teeth plus five teeth equals nine teeth.

Petrified teeth rarely ever spoil.

Deep in the ground
below the widgety grubs,

We found six T-Rex teeth,
little sharp, jagged nubs.

Four teeth plus six teeth equals ten teeth.

Carnivore teeth
aren't meant to chew shrubs.

Seven more teeth
in an old bunny lair.

They'd be a tasty snack
if T-Rex were still here.

Four teeth plus seven teeth equals eleven teeth.

These lucky rabbits
can sleep without care.

Far in the earth,
near a dung beetle's shell,

We find eight dino teeth,
ignoring the smell.

**Four teeth plus eight teeth
equals twelve teeth.**

Wash your hands
to stay well.

Way down deep in the dirt,
nine final teeth in a pile...

Somewhere there's a T-Rex
with lots of holes in his smile.

**Four teeth plus nine teeth
equals thirteen teeth.**

Our teeth might stretch for a mile.

"ARGHS!" Plus

While strolling the dock,
five pirates we passed.

We tried to say, "Hi" but they would have none of that.

Argh!" said five pirates, in a loud and clear song.
Saying "Hi" to a pirate was nothing but wrong.

No "Arghs!" we had heard...

Now we heard five.

Five "Arghs!" plus zero "Arghs!" equals five "Arghs!"

Then more pirates arrived.

One pirate clopped up, as his peg leg hit the pier.

He "Arghed!" to the five pirates.
All "Arghed!" back in his ear.

Five "Arghs!" plus one "Argh!" equals six "Arghs!"

Two pirates walked up,
parrots perched on their shoulders so bright.

They "Arghed!" the five pirates,
Five "Arghed!" back with delight.

Five "Arghs!" plus two "Arghs!" equals seven "Arghs!"

The parrots just squawked...

About crackers and night.

Three scraggly pirates, ears pierced, swaggered close.

They "Arghed!" our five pirates.
Who "Arghed!" back like a toast.

Five "Arghs!" plus three
"Arghs!" equals eight "Arghs!"

The three joined their ship...

The Buccaneer's Ghost.

Four tattooed pirates come out of the mist.

They "Arghed!" the five pirates,
who "Arghed!" back hard as a fist.

Five "Arghs!" plus four "Arghs!"
equals nine "Arghs!"

A tight crooked smile...

Meant they all got the gist.

Five crusty pirates approached with a sneer.

Till five "Arghs!" meet five "Arghs!" now there was nothing to fear.

Five "Arghs!" plus five "Arghs!" equals ten "Arghs!"

Off into port...

They head free and clear.

Six pirates darted up, with swords close at hand.

But "Argh!" in salute,
five "Arghs!" returned by the clan.

Five "Arghs!" plus six "Arghs!"
equals eleven "Arghs!"

The six moved on with their plan.

Seven pirates with poles went, "Argh!" out to go fish.

The five "Arghed!" right back, fulfilling their wish.

Five "Arghs!" plus seven "Arghs!" equals twelve "Arghs!"

If they bring back a catch...

Pirates will all share in the dish.

Eight lanky pirates walked by with a chest.

"Argh!" to the five. They "Argh!" back all their best.

Five "Arghs!" plus eight "Arghs!" equals thirteen "Arghs!"

Pirates spent some of their treasure..

And buried the rest.

Finally, nine pirates "Argh!" up with glee.

"Argh!" back five pirates, their mates were set free.

Five "Arghs!" plus nine "Arghs!" equals fourteen "Arghs!"

Up the gangway, all aboard!

It's "Argh" out to sea!

LORIKEET LANDINGS
Plus 6

I love the zoo. It's always a treat.

And which animal is first? It has to be the Lorikeet.

They're not in a cage, but surrounded by nets.

You get to walk right in, just like they're your pets.

Pick up some nectar. A zookeeper puts it in a cup.

Then see what happens when you hold that cup up.

Ah, six lorikeets just landed on me.

Zero lorikeets plus six lorikeets equals six lorikeets.

They perch on your body.

They drink nectar with glee.

One more lorikeet flies down for a sip...

Joining the six to take a small nip.

Six lorikeets plus one lorikeet equals seven lorikeets.

Hold your hand steady...

So the nectar won't tip.

One flies away, his bird belly full.

Two more land with the six,
and my shirt starts to pull.

Six lorikeets plus two lorikeets equals eight lorikeets.

Two take flight,
three birds safely land...

With the six on my arm,
shoulder, head, and hand.

Six lorikeets plus three lorikeets equals nine lorikeets.

Three finish eating.

They fly off to the sand.

Four new lorikeets
wrap their feet round my hair.

Joining the six
who are already there.

**Six lorikeets plus four lorikeets
equals ten lorikeets.**

Four well-fed birds

Jump back in the air.

But five more bird talons grip into my flesh.

Add them to the six, eating nectar so fresh.

**Six lorikeets plus five lorikeets
equals eleven lorikeets.**

Then five fly away,

Back to the mesh.

Fill up my cup, because here come six more.

With the six on your shoulder, you're a lorikeet store.

Six lorikeets plus six lorikeets equals twelve lorikeets.

Keep your mouth closed,

They might think it's a door.

Seven lorikeets just landed on my back.

With six on your front, it's a lorikeet hunger attack.

Six lorikeets plus seven lorikeets equals thirteen lorikeets.

Then seven fly off,

To digest their snack.

Eight lorikeets just jumped on my arm.

Don't scare them or the six by showing alarm.

Six lorikeets plus eight lorikeets, equals fourteen lorikeets.

Eight stuffed birds fly away,

Knowing you meant them no harm.

Nine lorikeets are flapping my way,

When they land with a thud, will the other six stay?

Six lorikeets plus nine lorikeets equals fifteen lorikeets.

Can you add up all the lorikeets' feet before they fly away?

SEVEN MOLDY MUFFINS

Plus 7

Yummy! Mommy brought home muffins.

Open the box! Let's eat!

UGH! Seven moldy muffins is in no way a treat!

NO muffins–we now have the seven moldy kind.

Our taste buds they cry. It's such a gross find.

$$7 + 0 = 7$$

Dad comes in the door. A muffin in his bag.

Please, let us have it! We beg and we nag.

Yikes! It's moldy too!

It's black and it's hairy!

A stale, mucky goo.

$$7 + 1 = 8$$

Aunt Lou joins us now. She has two muffins in her purse.

They have to be better – the seven are worse!

$$7 + 2 = 9$$

"Three muffins she has hidden," says dear sister Kate.

In the cupboard, let's hurry! I'm too hungry to wait.

$$7 + 3 = 10$$

Cousin Kurt joins the fray, "I've got four in the car."

Is the car right outside? Is it near? Is it far?

$$7 + 4 = 11$$

Are there no good muffins anywhere in this town?

"I've got five in the oven," Grandma says, her frown upside down.

$$7 + 5 = 12$$

There are six by the TV – I remember way back.

But they're gross, and they're hairy, and the bottoms are black.

7 + 6 = 13

Seven muffins I saw on the neighbors front porch.

We run out to look, and they're covered with spores.

7 + 7 = 14

I can't decide if I'm hungry or sick.

All these bad muffins, and the mold is quite thick.

"I have eight muffins," adds our old nanny Dee.
"And not one bit of mold can anyone see."

We hurriedly grab them, and break them apart.
And each one, like the seven, is moldy at heart.

7 + 8 =15

Wait, here comes our uncle, the baker and cook.

He must have fresh muffins. We could give them a look.

We open the package, our mouths are all water.

And nine moldy muffins,

Send our dreams to the slaughter.

7 + 9 = 16

All these moldy muffins,
I'm queasy down to my legs.

Maybe we should just ask
Mom to scramble some
eggs.

EIGHT TINY "RAIN" DEER

Plus 8

Still light after dinner, let's go to the park.

A few hours to play until the
sky will turn dark.

Outside to play on an evening so clear,

When what to my wondering
eyes should appear?

A dark cloud shaped like a sleigh,

And eight tiny "rain" deer.

**Eight huge deer-shaped drops falling
from on high,**

And no more in sight all over the sky.

8 drops + 0 drops = 8 drops

I hope that it stops.

Down from above another 8 drops plunge.

One more drop hits my head
before I can lunge.

8 drops + 1 drop = 9 drops

My head is soaked like a sponge.

Another eight deer-shaped drops
fall from the sleigh.

Along with two more – should we
flee? Should we stay?

**8 drops + 2 drops = 10 drops.
This oddly- shaped rain has ruined our play.**

Eight more drops coming fast,

With three in their wake.

8 drops + 3 drops = 11 drops. How much more can we take?

Four "rain" deer drops is all that I see.

The other eight drops, they hit a big tree.

8 drops + 4 drops = 12 drops

Plants need the water, so
it's okay with me.

Here come eight more tiny "rain" deer,

With five of their friends
dropping right near.

8 drops + 5 drops = 13 drops

Soaking my shoes, when I didn't get clear,

Another eight drops – what a weird kind of rain,

And six more behind, like a little
deer train.

8 drops + 6 drops = 14 drops

The drops are so big, they
sink down to my brain.

It is not over yet. Eight
more drops come down.

Plus, seven more drops go
splat on the ground.

8 drops + 7 drops = 15 drops

Fwap! On the dirt with a cool little sound.

Then eight drops come next.

And eight more join the team.

8 drops + 8 drops = 16 drops

All the wet cars are starting to gleam.

Eight tiny "rain" deer once more jump from the sleigh.

Another nine spill from the cloud, joining in the fray.

8 drops + 9 drops = 17 drops

Does it look like this cloud might be going away?

Nope, I believe the little caribou have washed out our day.

SMELLY CATS TO THE NINES

Plus 9

Smelly Cats! Smelly Cats!

Boy, do they stink!

There's nine in the closet.

I see one in the sink.

Smelly cats everywhere –
What should we do?

We could add them all up.

Pinch our noses
'til they're through!

Nine in the closet
plus one in the sink.
That's ten smelly cats.
We don't dare take a drink.

There are two on the bed.

Getting gross hair on the sheets.

9 plus 2 equals 11.

They smell worse than your feet.

Three fetid felines, curled up in the shower.

They'll curl your toes, with great stinky power.

9 plus 3 equals 12.
The odor gets worse and worse by the hour.

Four cruddy kitties, in the desk fast asleep.

Their stench up the wall has started to creep.

9 plus 4 equals 13.
Lunch in my belly, I am trying to keep.

Five on the washer.

Six near the vase.

Rancid smelly cats all over the place.
9 plus 5 equals 14.
9 plus 6 equals 15.
How many smelly cats have yet to be seen?

Seven cats in the trash.

Eight by the phone.

The air is so foul, it seeps through skin down to bone.
9 plus 7 equals 16.
9 plus 8 equals 17.

It would take a sandblaster to get this house clean.

I can't believe my eyes, not to mention my nose.

Nine more smelly cats hiding under the clothes.

9 plus 9 equals 18.

Now, if you paid attention,

and your mind is quite quick,

You've noticed a way to add nines that is a neat little trick.

Adding by nine is like
adding by ten,

except the answer is one less
when you get to the end.

9 + 1 is the same as 10 + 0 = 10

9 + 2 is the same as 10 + 1 = 11
9 + 3 is the same as 10 + 2 = 12

9 + 4 = 10 + 3 = 13
9 + 5 = 10 + 4 = 14

9 + 6 = 10 + 5 = 15
9 + 7 = 10 + 6 = 16

9 + 8 = 10 + 7 = 17
9 + 9 = 10 + 8 = 18

But don't sniff the kitties.

You just might get sick.

TEN TEXTS

Plus 10

My sister is a teen and has her first phone.

It has games and a camera. She just won't leave it alone.

But of all the new tools and Apps that are "next,"

Her favorite thing is to send a quick text.

My sister can send ten texts with lighting-fast speed.

Can any of her friends keep up with that feed?

She first sends ten texts to Jenny from Math.

But gets none back, could she be in the bath?

10 texts + 0 texts = 10 texts.

When they meet face-to-face, Jenny might suffer text wrath.

So, out go ten texts to Barbi right quick.

Only one text comes back,
does she not know the trick?

10 texts + 1 text = 11 texts.

Are Barbi's thumbs way too thick?

Ten texts more in a flash out to Sue,

But only two texts come back,
that's not even a few.

10 texts + 2 texts = 12 texts.

What is a brilliant text-er to do?

Send out ten more texts to Katy McGruell.

But only three texts come back.
Is Katy low on fuel?

10 texts + 3 texts = 13 texts.

This isn't a very strong texting duel.

Sis sends ten texts lickity-split.

All to Noel, who sends back
only four and that's it.

10 texts + 4 texts = 14 texts.

Can no one keep up
with her even one bit?

Not to give up, ten texts zip to Loraine,

Who sends back only five like a
slow-moving train.

10 texts + 5 texts = 15 texts.

Is there anyone who can
keep up with Sister's brain?

Maybe a boy, ten texts out to Trent,

When six texts come
back, we are above 50%!

10 texts + 6 texts = 16 texts.

On the right track, let's text one more gent.

Out go ten texts to computer geek Pete.

Who sends back seven texts, some say with his feet.

10 texts + 7 foot texts = 17 texts.

It looks like the boys can compete.

Ten texts to Wes with the speed of the Flash,

Eight texts come back in a mad texting dash.

10 texts + 8 texts = 18 texts.

When adults try to text, the whole system can crash.

One last friend, Sis sends ten texts to Claire.

Nine texts bounce right back, gigabytes zip through the air.

10 texts + 9 texts = 19 texts.

Sister's new texting buddy has now become clear.

Happily now, Claire gets ten more texts from dear Sis.

Claire sends back 35, can you add that to 10 with nary a miss?

ELEVEN DRUMMERS DRUMMING

Plus 11

Hey, KNOCK, KNOCK, look what's
coming up the street.

It's eleven men with drums
all keeping to the beat.

11 + 0 = 11

BANG, TA-TA, BOOM, I am
tapping with my feet.

But, TAPPA, TAPPA, TOM-
TOM, another man joins in.

One more with the eleven
and the fun can begin.

11 + 1 = 12

The one he leaves BANG,
BANG, BANG, back to
eleven again.

RAT-A-TAT here come two more,
to join up where one left.

11 + 2 = 13

Two with eleven, SNAP, SNAP,
SNAP, gives the beat some heft.

The two break off, SPLIT, SPLIT,
SPLIT and three join the line.

11 + 3 = 14

Three with eleven, BAM, BAM, BAM, the beat is feeling fine.

TANG, TANG the three walk away, and four join the fray.

11 + 4 = 15

Four with eleven, BAP-BOP-BOOM, those drummers sure can play.

SNAP, SNAP, the four slip away and five drummers add their sticks.

11 + 5 = 16

Five with eleven, they all keep the time with BAMS and BOOMS and CLICKS.

The five pull away TICK, CRASH, KABOOM, and are soon replaced by six.

$$11 + 6 = 17$$

Six with eleven, SNARE-TAP-TING, a very happy mix.

But the six don't stay, and seven drum up with a TAM, TAM, DROP.

$$11 + 7 = 18$$

Seven with eleven, CLANG-DANG-A-CHANG, the beat it just won't stop.

But stop does the seven, BASH, BANG, SWOP, replaced
by a new drumming eight.

$$11 + 8 = 19$$

Eight drum with eleven, thumping in time, the
THUMP, THUMP, THUMP is great.

Then eight go away and eleven join nine, all in a line.

$$11 + 9 = 20$$

Twenty drummers banging in time, RAP-TAP-SNAP, and then they stop on a dime.

MY PET DUST MITE

Minus 9

Way down in my bed,
Too small to be seen,
Lives my pet dust mite
Named Harvey McSheen.

We feed him at night
While I roll round the bed,
My dead skins cells fall off
Right on top of his head.

He chews up our skin,
Till the sheets are all clear.
He has millions of friends that make our cells disappear.

We can subtract all the skin
As it's chomped out of sight.
A wonderful math game
For a dark, stormy night.

Nine dead skin cells drop right in front of his face.
He gobbles one up, leaving eight in their place.

Nine minus one equals eight.

But Harvey's still hungry. He can eat so much more.
Then nine more dead skin cells fall toward the floor.
Harvey is quick. His hunger is great,
He scarfs two from the nine, leaving seven on his plate.

Nine minus two equals seven.

Nine more are coming. Harvey licks his mite lips.
And chomps down three skin cells, leaving six salt-covered chips.

Nine minus three equals six.

I roll onto my back. Nine more dead cells flake off.
Harvey chows down four like a pig from a trough.

How many cells did Harvey not eat?

Nine minus four equals five.

Then night's wearing on. I scratch at my ear.

And nine lifeless skin cells, to Harvey fall near.

One big old bite and he swallows up five.

Four little skin cells to the floor start to dive.

Nine minus five equals four.

I twiddle my toes. Nine cells fall from the sky.

Harvey swallows up six, leaving three left to fly.

Nine minus six equals three.

A flick of my chin, nine more cells hit the air.

Into Harvey's mouth go seven, only two left to spare.

Nine minus seven equals two.

A stretch of my arms, a pat of my legs,

Nine dead skins cells drop, like a dog Harvey begs.

He opens his mite mouth, gulps down an eight skin cell treat.

A smack and a grin,
leaving one little cell at his feet.

Nine minus eight equals one.

The sun almost up,
A new day to begin.

I yawn nice and loud.
Nine cells fall off my shin.

One last big meal,
Harvey's done for the night.

He chomps down all nine,
Leaving nothing in sight.

Nine minus nine equals zero.

I start the day,
Harvey goes to sleep.

All my dead skin cells,
In his belly they heap.

About the Authors

Janet Lynne (Hagemeyer) Tassell, Ph.D.

After time in the classroom teaching mathematics, Janet spent 14 years as a Director of Learning and Assessment working with K-12 teachers in curriculum and professional development. During this time, she worked closely with a literacy coordinator discovering the connections between reading and mathematics comprehension strategies. This fostered a growing love for literature in mathematics where she continued to search for ways to help students learn mathematics through reading. A one time ESL coordinator and a Gifted Education coordinator, this idea of math AND reading fluency to help students of limited English proficiency with the partner reading format yet also using fun vocabulary by challenging those from a gifted angle, shows how she incorporates her experience from her career in this book. She now is an Assistant Professor at Western Kentucky University in Bowling Green, Kentucky, where she teaches Elementary Math Methods and directs the Elementary Math Specialist Endorsement program. She is the co-director of the Toyota Math and Technology Leadership Academy and the professional devolopment coordinator for Project GEMS (Gifted Education for Math and Science).

Brad Lee Tassell

Brad Tassell is an award winning, best selling author and comedian. He has won 3 Pinnacle awards for his programs for children and teachers. His character education picture book Billy Fustertag Learns Comedy helps struggling readers in grades 1-2. He is married to Dr. Janet Tassell and they have one brilliant daughter named Darby.

About The Artist

Nathan Hendricksen

Nathan Hendricksen is a graduate of the visual arts program at the University of Kentucky. He lives in Bowling Green Kentucky with his wife and a fat beagle.